My Flashback 30th Birthday Quiz Book

Turning 30 Humor for People Born in the '90s USA

by JEST FEST

This paperback second edition first published in 2022 by Life in Puzzle.

Copyright © Jest Fest, 2022.

2   4   6   8   10   9   7   5   3   1

ISBN: 978-3-948706-63-0

The INNARDS

PART 1 – CHILDHOOD
Things Only '90s Kids Will Remember
Toon Anagrams
Toy Number Puzzle Picture
Best Girl's Names
Movie Search
Funfair Riddler
Sweet Sudoku
Family Flicks
Cool Crossword
Best Boy's Names
Delicious Desserts
Muddy Memory

PART 2 – TEENHOOD
Things Only '00s Teens Will Remember
Complete the Lyrics
Groovy Crossword
Name the Movie 1
Behind the Times Sudoku
The Odd Couple
Famous Whodunnit
Spot the Difference
Fave Gadget Maze
Song Search
Pastime NPP
Name the Movie 2
Past Price Is Right

PART 3 – The ANSWER KEY

BONUS BIRTHDAY BADGE

MORE FROM Life in Puzzle

WACKY WORLD NEWS 1990-2009

Love the puzzles? Want more?

Scan the QR code or go to
lifeinpuzzle.com and grab your FREE
printable copy of "Hilarious Joke Book
Sudoku: A Brain-teasing Collection Of
50 Funny Puzzles"

THE FIRST 30 YEARS OF CHILDHOOD

PART 1:
CHILDHOOD

Things Only 90s Kids Will Remember

A ton of cool stuff debuted in the 90s and 90s kids were the first generation to enjoy them.

But even though you lived through it, it's easy to forget all the things that made the 90s truly unique.

So, get your pen ready for nostalgia-filled puzzles that will bring back your childhood memories from the 90s!

ARE ALWAYS THE HARDEST

THE FIRST 30 YEARS OF CHILDHOOD

Toon Anagrams

Rearrange these phrases to reveal some great cartoons you probably watched growing up in the '90s.

Rag Rust

Answer: _____

Brat Dee Sorry A Lot x

Answer: _____

Bank Hint Deny Pair

Answer: _____

ARE ALWAYS THE HARDEST

Toy Number Puzzle Picture

In any order you wish, copy the contents of each square in the jumbled picture below to the same numbered square in the blank grid on the next page until the entire puzzle is done, then add vivid '90s shades to your masterpiece.

6	31	2	37	0	1	27	60
24	58	13	53	29	21	14	44
16	17	36	50	20	5	43	4
8	42	3	15	49	34	12	26
45	51	62	35	40	38	7	41
18	25	32	39	56	61	46	55
48	28	52	30	19	57	54	11
63	10	9	59	22	47	33	23

0	1	2	3	4	5	6	7
8	9	10	11	12	13	14	15
16	17	18	19	20	21	22	23
24	25	26	27	28	29	30	31
32	33	34	35	36	37	38	39
40	41	42	43	44	45	46	47
48	49	50	51	52	53	54	55
56	57	58	59	60	61	62	63

ARE ALWAYS THE HARDEST

Best Girl's Names

These were the 10 most popular names given to baby girls in the 1990s and no doubt you met a few girls with these names growing up.

See if you can guess the top three and in the right order. Write the names on the dotted lines across the page.

Emily

Elizabeth

Samantha

Jessica

Taylor

Megan

Brittany

Ashley

Sarah

Amanda

THE FIRST 30 YEARS OF CHILDHOOD

1

....

2   3

....

ARE ALWAYS THE HARDEST

Movie Search

The titles of four kids' movies from the '90s that defined your childhood are hidden below. Can you find and circle them?

```
H   O   M   E   W   A   R   D   Y   B   O   U   N   D

H   O   M   E   W   A   R   D   Y   B   O   U   N   D

H   O   M   E   W   A   R   D   Y   B   O   U   N   D

H   O   M   E   W   A   R   D   Y   B   O   U   N   D

H   O   M   E   W   A   T   D   Y   B   O   U   N   D

H   O   G   N   I   K   N   O   I   L   E   H   T   D

H   O   M   E   W   A   R   D   Y   B   O   U   N   D

H   O   M   E   W   A   R   D   Y   S   O   U   N   D

H   O   M   Y   W   A   R   D   Y   B   T   U   N   D

H   O   M   E   G   A   R   D   Y   B   O   O   N   D

H   O   M   E   W   I   R   D   Y   B   O   U   R   D

H   O   M   E   W   A   R   D   Y   B   O   U   N   Y

H   O   M   E   W   A   R   L   Y   B   O   U   N   D

M   A   J   E   C   A   P   S   Y   B   O   U   N   D

H   O   M   E   W   A   R   D   Y   B   O   U   N   D
```

THE FIRST 30 YEARS OF CHILDHOOD

Funfair Riddler

Rearrange these phrases to reveal some unforgettable fairground games.

Sortings

Answer: _____

Elk Bales

Answer: _____

Kodak Ouch

Answer: _____

On Pablo Pol

Answer: _____

I Plonk

Answer: _____

ARE ALWAYS THE HARDEST

Sweet Sudoku

Fill in the blank squares so that each row, each column, and each 3-by-3 block contain the letters A, C, G, H, I, N, R, T, X.

The letters you produce from the highlighted squares completes the following phrase to describe you:

"AS A '90s KID, I LOVED EATING S_____ T_____"

A	H	T				R		G
			A				N	H
	I		H	G	R			
T	A					N		
	N	H	C		G	X	I	
		G					C	A
			R	C	H	G	A	X
G	R				T			
H		X				T		I

Turn to page 40

THE FIRST 30 YEARS OF CHILDHOOD

Family Flicks

Test your creative thinking skills with these challenging letter puzzles. The theme is popular 1990s family-friendly films.

1. Which letter is three to the right of the letter immediately to the left of the letter that is four to the left of the second letter O?

H O M E A L O N E

2. I am a 7-letter '90s family comedy.
5, 4, 6 = the top of a jar
2, 6, 7, 1 = the first man
1, 7, 6 = angry or cross
What movie am I?

3. What letter should replace the question mark in this star?

Cool Crossword

Test your knowledge of popular children's toys, books, breakfast cereals, and drinks from the '90s.

1. A line of cute and very collectable stuffed toys.

2. A book about Eddy's adventure in the woods to find something he lost.

3. A whole-grain cereal consisting of small, chocolate cereal balls.

4. A book about selfishness and sharing and the distinctive shiny foil scales of a certain aquatic animal.

5. A tangy orange drink containing water, high fructose corn syrup and less than 2% concentrated fruit juice.

6. A playground game using small, round, cartoon-adorned milk caps, often collected and traded.

7. Grab-n-go soft-baked breakfast bars with fruit middles that you ate for lunch.

8. A lemonade-looking, cola-tasting drink to rot your teeth without staining them.

9. A book about a little hare's attempts to show his affection for his daddy.

10. A cereal like Rice Krispies but named after the three grains it composed of: corn, wheat, and rice.

11. A soda formulated especially for kids and sold in tiny, "plump" bottles.

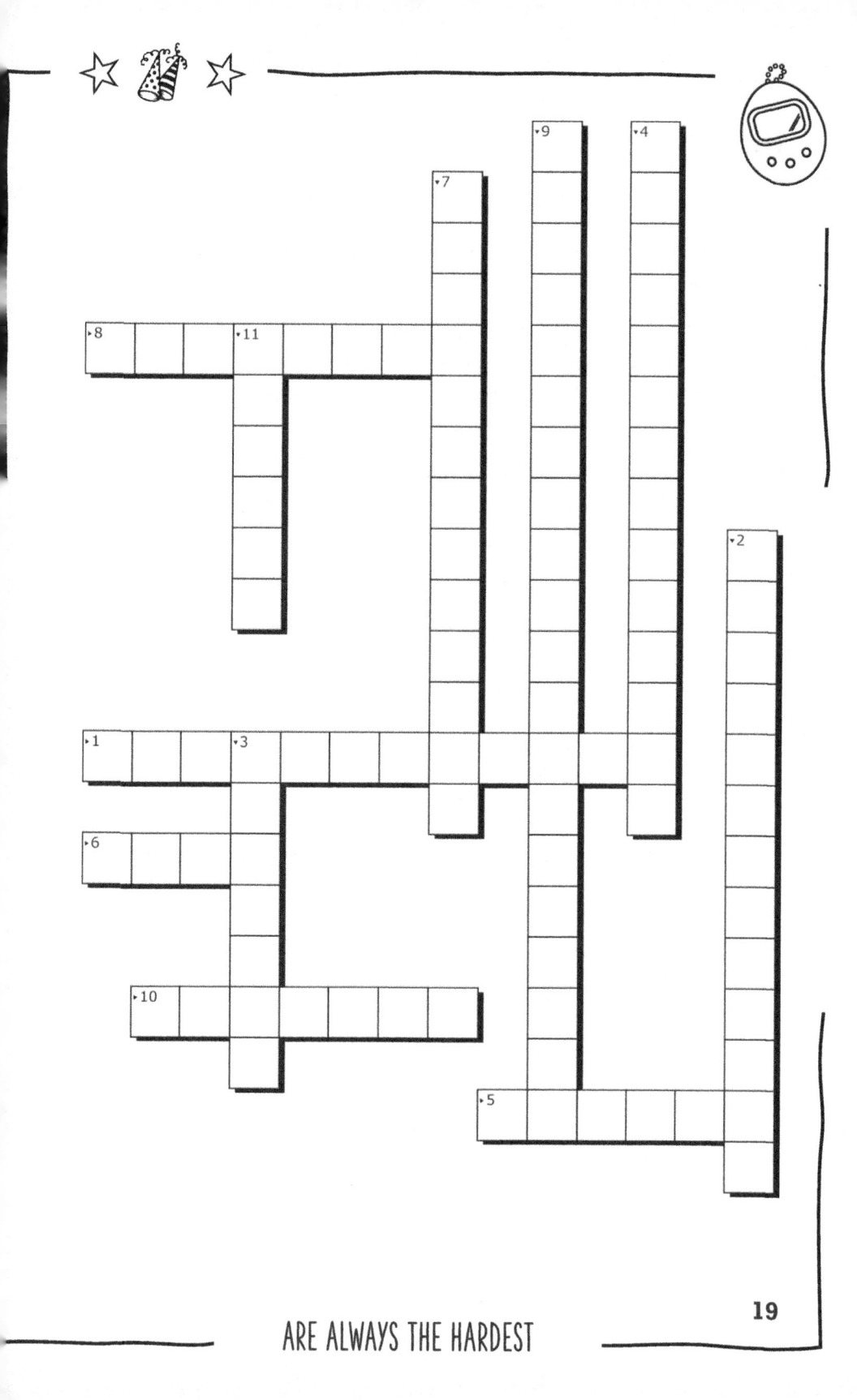

ARE ALWAYS THE HARDEST

Best Boy's Names

These were the 10 most popular names given to baby boys in the 1990s and no doubt you met a few boys with these names growing up.

See if you can guess the top three and in the right order. Write the names on the dotted lines across the page.

Matthew

Jacob

Andrew

Nicholas

Tyler

Christopher

Joseph

Michael

Joshua

Daniel

1

....

2 3

....

ARE ALWAYS THE HARDEST

Delicious Dessert

Nothing brings back memories like the sweets of a '90s childhood. See if you can guess the popular '90s dessert from just the ingredients below...without feeling hungry!

Reconstituted skimmed milk
Coconut oil
Glucose-fructose syrup
Sugar
Water
Glucose syrup
Whey solids (milk)
Fat reduced cocoa powder
Emulsifiers (mono- and di-glycerides of fatty acids, ammonium phosphatides)
Stabilizers (locust bean gum, guar gum, carrageenan)
Flavoring
May contain soy

CLUE: The ingredients were formed in several rippled layers of ___ separated by thin layers of sprayed-on compound ___. It is now available in many flavors, including mint, but it's the original that will surely take your tastebuds on a trip down memory lane.

Answer: _____

Muddy Memory

Science has found that as you age, your memory becomes more like a pathological liar, often giving you rose-tinted views of childhood and recollections of events that never even happened.

Let's put your 30-year-old brain to the test. Which of the following four images matches exactly with the balloon image at the start of this book?

Note Space

Use these pages if you need to jot something down when solving the puzzles and riddles in this section.

THE FIRST 30 YEARS OF CHILDHOOD

ARE ALWAYS THE HARDEST

Turn to page 66

THE FIRST 30 YEARS OF CHILDHOOD

ARE ALWAYS THE HARDEST

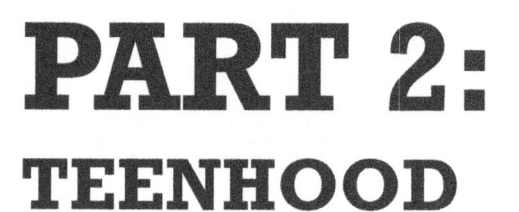 

PART 2:
TEENHOOD

Things Only 00s Teens Will Remember

Although everything changes when you become a teenager no matter when and where you were born, the world in the 00s was a very different place than it is today.

We all know you enjoyed plenty of the usual coming-of-age experiences on your journey to adulthood. When you hit your teens, your taste in clothes, hairstyles, and music all changed.

With pen still in hand, it's time to see how well you remember the groovy stuff that defined your millennial adolescence.

THE FIRST 30 YEARS OF CHILDHOOD

Complete the Lyrics

Nobody writes songs like they did in the '00s. Fill in the blanks below with the correct lyrics and prove yourself a '00s music expert.

"So, I got up and followed her to the _____

She said, baby let's go

When I told her (let's go!) I said

_____!"

"Never made it as a _____ man

I couldn't cut it as a poor man _____

Tired of living like a _____ man

I'm sick of sight without a sense of _____"

"I'm gonna fight 'em all

A _____ _____ army couldn't hold me back

They're gonna _____ ____ _____

Taking their _____ right behind my back"

Groovy Crossword

Test your knowledge of iconic fashion trends, hairstyles, magazines, and dance crazes from the '00s.

1. The quintessential teenage boy's hairstyle made famous by Zac Efron and Justin Bieber.
2. A pink-shaded accessory to give your lips a shimmery finish that you kept in the back pocket of your jeans.
3. A dance craze given to us by Mr. C the Slide Man that's perfect for aerobics classes.
4. A style of denim pants that were great for flaunting your midriff (and your underwear).
5. A free, expressive, and exaggerated street dance the evolved from Clown Dancing or C-Walkin.
6. The teenage spin-off of Cosmopolitan, targeted at teenage girls and featuring fashion and celebrities.
7. Soulja Boy served up this noughties classic that became a hit across school hallways and car parks.
8. Once rocked by David Beckham, this hairstyle required shaved sides and a scruffy strip of hair in the middle (sometimes dyed).
9. A brand of headwear that a stylish trucker would accessorize with.
10. A popular girl's hairstyle with the bangs/fringe clipped back just over the forehead and teased to make it as "poufy" as possible.

THE FIRST 30 YEARS OF CHILDHOOD

ARE ALWAYS THE HARDEST

Name the Movie 1

Guess the classic movies that '00s teens adored from these legendary quotes.

"He is the cheese to my macaroni."

_____

"That is so fetch!"

_____

"I hope that when the world comes to an end, I can breathe a sigh of relief, because there will be so much to look forward to."

_____

"Jenna, if you're gonna start lying about your age, I'd go with 27."

_____

"Our great mother does not take sides, Jake; she protects the balance of life."

_____

THE FIRST 30 YEARS OF CHILDHOOD

Behind the Times Sudoku

Fill in the blank squares so that each row, each column, and each 3-by-3 block contain the letters A, B, C, E, L, R, S, U, Y.

The letters you produce from the highlighted squares completes the following phrase to describe you:

"AS A '00s TEEN, I THOUGHT _____ _____S WERE COOL!"

Y		C	R	░	░	░	S	
	B		E			C		A
L							B	
A			L	S				C
			Y		U			
U				R	C			Y
	C			░		░		S
R		S		U		B		
	L				S	E		U

The Odd Couple

These celebrities got hitched in the '00s, but which couple didn't get the happily ever after they were hoping for and split before the decade's end?

Britney & KFed

Tom & Katie

Angelina & Brad

Famous Whodunnit

They were legends and true gods of music in the '00s. But one of them took things too far backstage and ate all the brown M&Ms.

After arguing for hours and missing their performance, the police were called and interrogated the five suspects. Can you guess the guilty party if only three of the following statements are true?

1. Justin: 'JC did it.'

2. Lance: 'It wasn't me.'

3. Joey: 'Chris is innocent.'

4. JC: 'Justin is lying when he accuses me.'

5. Chris: 'Lance is telling the truth.'

Answer: _____

Spot the Difference

How good were you at using Bunsen burners, pipettes, test tubes, and microscopes in school? Now see how good you are at spotting the 6 subtle differences in these tricky photos. Good luck!

THE FIRST 30 YEARS OF CHILDHOOD

ARE ALWAYS THE HARDEST

Fave Gadget Maze

What a great decade for technology! Quickly and without thinking, select and trace a dotted line A, B or C along the path to reveal what your subconscious thinks was the best gadget of the '00s.

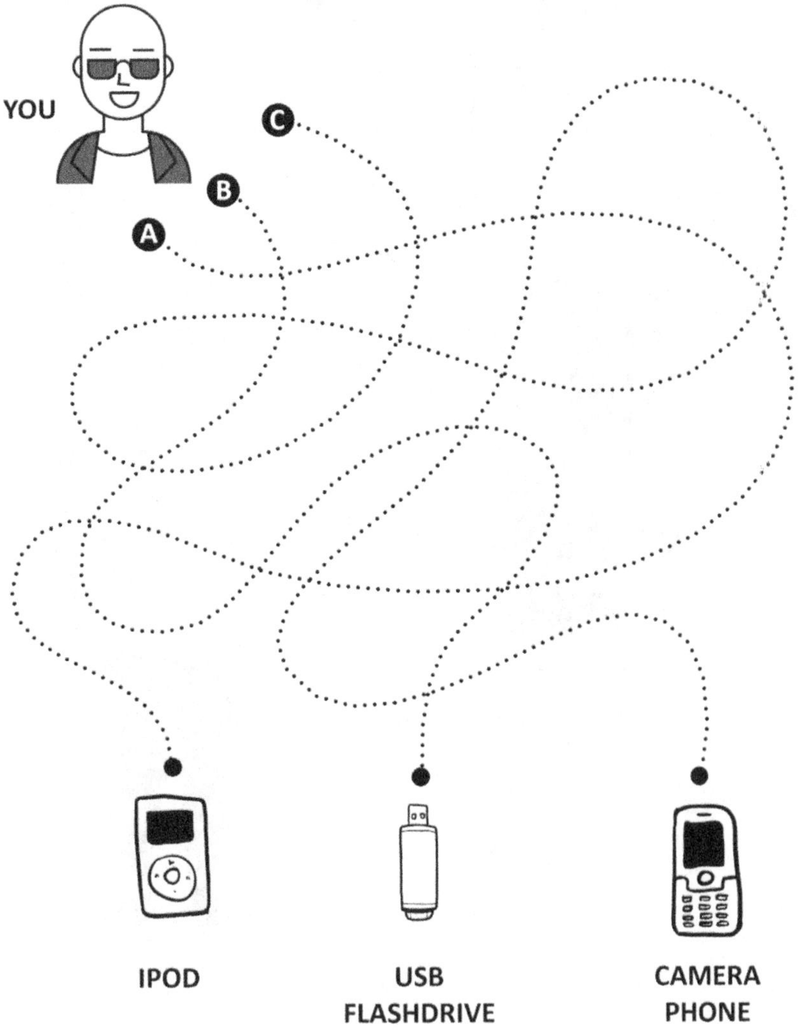

YOU

C

B

A

IPOD

USB FLASHDRIVE

CAMERA PHONE

Turn to page 26

Song Search

The titles of six best-selling songs from the '00s that had you busting a move at the school disco are hidden below. Can you find and circle them?

```
A  I  L  E  V  A  P  H  H  B  Q  V  V  H
V  D  U  R  L  Z  U  R  M  N  T  Y  O  A
Z  Q  U  E  X  J  X  V  L  A  F  W  N  V
F  P  Z  D  Q  H  J  M  V  C  Y  Z  X  K
J  R  E  G  G  I  D  D  L  O  G  A  L  G
L  S  L  S  B  V  F  I  U  X  T  N  N  O
E  R  Q  X  O  H  U  R  V  B  H  I  J  M
T  J  T  Y  Q  L  E  V  P  H  L  R  S  J
M  U  F  W  M  M  O  U  Z  E  U  Y  P  Y
E  I  H  Z  I  K  R  J  E  D  X  T  M  D
L  B  Y  N  J  L  S  F  N  D  M  U  N  J
O  Y  D  P  O  B  A  E  C  Q  J  Z  A  T
V  M  X  W  N  T  V  M  D  E  L  Z  A  I
E  O  Z  Q  T  Z  I  L  N  H  Y  I  Q  K
Y  K  B  O  K  Y  T  P  X  S  D  J  W  P
O  R  G  M  G  B  U  L  C  A  D  N  I  J
U  I  E  O  Y  E  V  D  B  F  T  O  S  B
```

ARE ALWAYS THE HARDEST

Pastime NPP

In any order you wish, copy the contents of each square in the jumbled picture below to the same numbered square in the blank grid on the next page until the entire puzzle is done, then add vivid '00s shades to your masterpiece.

THE FIRST 30 YEARS OF CHILDHOOD

0	1	2	3	4	5	6	7
8	9	10	11	12	13	14	15
16	17	18	19	20	21	22	23
24	25	26	27	28	29	30	31
32	33	34	35	36	37	38	39
40	41	42	43	44	45	46	47
48	49	50	51	52	53	54	55
56	57	58	59	60	61	62	63

ARE ALWAYS THE HARDEST

Name the Movie 2

Guess the classic movies that '00s teens adored from these legendary quotes.

"It doesn't even have a first name – it just says McLovin!"

"Go f**k yourself San Diego!"

"Please bore someone else with your questions."

"You're impossibly fast, and strong. Your skin is pale white and ice cold. Your eyes change color, and sometimes you speak like – like you're from a different time."

"Even the smallest person can change the course of the future."

Past Price Is Right

The cost of stuff skyrocketed in recent times. But can you guess how much these young adult essentials cost in the '00s?

-------- Cinema Ticket --------

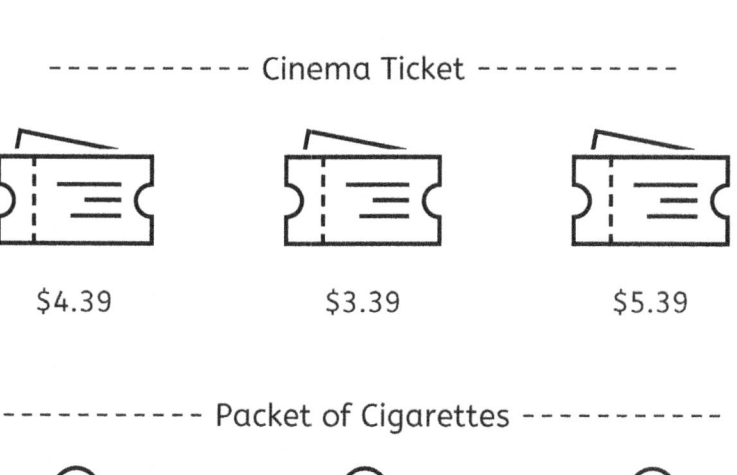

$4.39 $3.39 $5.39

-------- Packet of Cigarettes --------

$3.89 $2.19 $4.69

-------- Six-pack of Beer --------

$4.92 $6.32 $5.72

Note Space

Use these pages if you need to jot something down when solving the puzzles and riddles in this section.

ARE ALWAYS THE HARDEST

ARE ALWAYS THE HARDEST

THE FIRST 30 YEARS OF CHILDHOOD

PART 3:
The ANSWER KEY

Let's see how well you remember your past.

Toon Anagrams

Rearrange these phrases to reveal some great cartoons you probably watched growing up in the '90s.

Rag Rust

Answer: <u>Rugrats</u>

Brat Dee Sorry A Lot x

Answer: <u>Dexter's Laboratory</u>

Bank Hint Deny Pair

Answer: <u>Pinky and the Brain</u>

ARE ALWAYS THE HARDEST

Toy Number Puzzle Picture

In any order you wish, copy the contents of each square in the jumbled picture below to the same numbered square in the blank grid on the next page until the entire puzzle is done, then add vivid '90s shades to your masterpiece.

THE FIRST 30 YEARS OF CHILDHOOD

Best Girl's Names

These were the 10 most popular names given to baby girls in the 1990s and no doubt you met a few girls with these names growing up.

Here is the full list in the right order:

1	Jessica
2	Ashley
3	Emily

4	Sarah
5	Samantha
6	Amanda
7	Brittany
8	Elizabeth
9	Taylor
10	Megan

Movie Search

The titles of four kids' movies from the '90s that defined your childhood are hidden below. Can you find and circle them?

```
H  O  M  E  W  A  R  D  Y  B  O  U  N  D
H  O  M  E  W  A  R  D  Y  B  O  U  N  D
H  O  M  E  W  A  R  D  Y  B  O  U  N  D
H  O  M  E  W  A  R  D  Y  B  O  U  N  D
H  O  M  E  W  A  T  D  Y  B  O  U  N  D
H  O  G  N  I  K  N  O  I  L  E  H  T  D
H  O  M  E  W  A  R  D  Y  B  O  U  N  D
H  O  M  E  W  A  R  D  Y  S  O  U  N  D
H  O  M  Y  W  A  R  D  Y  B  T  U  N  D
H  O  M  E  G  A  R  D  Y  B  O  O  N  D
H  O  M  E  W  I  R  D  Y  B  O  U  R  D
H  O  M  E  W  A  R  D  Y  B  O  U  N  Y
H  O  M  E  W  A  R  L  Y  B  O  U  N  D
M  A  J  E  C  A  P  S  Y  B  O  U  N  D
H  O  M  E  W  A  R  D  Y  B  O  U  N  D
```

Funfair Riddler

Rearrange these phrases to reveal some unforgettable fairground games.

Sortings

Answer: Ring-Toss

Elk Bales

Answer: Skee-Ball

Kodak Ouch

Answer: Hook-a-Duck

On Pablo Pol

Answer: Balloon-Pop

I Plonk

Answer: Plinko

ARE ALWAYS THE HARDEST

Sweet Sudoku

Fill in the blank squares so that each row, each column, and each 3-by-3 block contain the letters A, C, G, H, I, N, R, T, X.

The letters you produce from the highlighted squares completes the following phrase to describe you:

"AS A '90s KID, I LOVED EATING <u>STRING</u> <u>THING</u>"

A	H	T	N	I	C	R	X	G
C	G	R	A	T	X	I	N	H
X	I	N	H	G	R	A	T	C
T	A	C	X	H	I	N	G	R
R	N	H	C	A	G	X	I	T
I	X	G	T	R	N	H	C	A
N	T	I	R	C	H	G	A	X
G	R	A	I	X	T	C	H	N
H	C	X	G	N	A	T	R	I

Cool Crossword

8 across: TAB CLEAR

1 across: BEANIE BABIES

6 across: POGS

10 across: TRIPLES

5 across: SUNNY

11 down: CHUBBY

7 down: NUTRIGRAINBAR

9 down: GUESSHOWMUCHILOVEYOU

4 down: THERAINBOWFISH

2 down: WHERESMYTED DY

3 down: NESQUUK

ARE ALWAYS THE HARDEST

Best Boy's Names

These were the 10 most popular names given to baby boys in the 1990s and no doubt you met a few boys with these names growing up.

Here is the full list in the right order:

1	Michael
2	Christopher
3	Matthew
----	----
4	Joshua
5	Jacob
6	Nicholas
7	Andrew
8	Daniel
9	Tyler
10	Joseph

THE FIRST 30 YEARS OF CHILDHOOD

Family Flicks

Test your creative thinking skills with these challenging letter puzzles. The theme is popular 1990s family-friendly films.

1. Which letter is three to the right of the letter immediately to the left of the letter that is four to the left of the second letter O?

H O M E A L O N E

2. I am a 7-letter '90s family comedy.
5, 4, 6 = the top of a jar
2, 6, 7, 1 = the first man
1, 7, 6 = angry or cross
What movie am I?
= MATILDA

3. What letter should replace the question mark in this star?
V. The letters spell the movie title "Beethoven"

Delicious Dessert

Nothing brings back memories like the sweets of a '90s childhood. See if you can guess the popular '90s dessert from just the ingredients below...without feeling hungry!

Reconstituted skimmed milk
Coconut oil
Glucose-fructose syrup
Sugar
Water
Glucose syrup
Whey solids (milk)
Fat reduced cocoa powder
Emulsifiers (mono- and di-glycerides of fatty acids, ammonium phosphatides)
Stabilizers (locust bean gum, guar gum, carrageenan)
Flavoring
May contain soy

CLUE: The ingredients were formed in several rippled layers of ___ separated by thin layers of sprayed-on compound ___. It is now available in many flavors, including mint, but it's the original that will surely take your tastebuds on a trip down memory lane.

Answer: Viennetta

Muddy Memory

Science has found that as you age, your memory becomes more like a pathological liar, often giving you rose-tinted views of childhood and recollections of events that never even happened.

Let's put your 30-year-old brain to the test. Which of the following four images matches exactly with the balloon image at the start of this book?

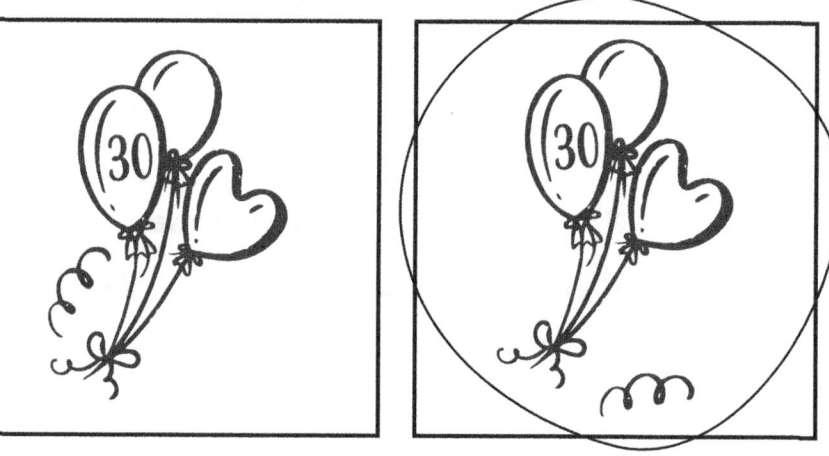

ARE ALWAYS THE HARDEST

Complete the Lyrics

Nobody writes songs like they did in the '00s. Fill in the blanks below with the correct lyrics and prove yourself a '00s music expert.

"So, I got up and followed her to the <u>floor</u>

She said, baby let's go

When I told her (let's go!) I said

<u>Yeah</u>!"

"Never made it as a <u>wise</u> man

I couldn't cut it as a poor man <u>stealing</u>

Tired of living like a <u>blind</u> man

I'm sick of sight without a sense of <u>feeling</u>"

"I'm gonna fight 'em all

A <u>seven nation</u> army couldn't hold me back

They're gonna <u>rip it off</u>

Taking their <u>time</u> right behind my back"

Groovy Crossword

8 Across: FAUXHAWK

7 Across: CRANKTHAT

2 Across: FROSTEDLIPGLOSS

3 Down: CACHACHASLIDE

9 Down: VODUTCHHAT

5 Down: CRUMPING

4 Down: LOWRISJEANS

6 Down: COSMOGIRL

10 Down: POUF

1 Down: SHAGGYSWOOP

ARE ALWAYS THE HARDEST

Name the Movie 1

Guess the classic movies that '00s teens adored from these legendary quotes.

"He is the cheese to my macaroni."

Juno

"That is so fetch!"

Mean Girls

"I hope that when the world comes to an end, I can breathe a sigh of relief, because there will be so much to look forward to."

Donnie Darko

"Jenna, if you're gonna start lying about your age, I'd go with 27."

13 Going on 30

"Our great mother does not take sides, Jake; she protects the balance of life."

Avatar

Turn to page 81

Behind the Times Sudoku

Fill in the blank squares so that each row, each column, and each 3-by-3 block contain the letters A, B, C, E, L, R, S, U, Y.

The letters you produce from the highlighted squares completes the following phrase to describe you:

"AS A '00s TEEN, I THOUGHT <u>BLU</u> <u>RAYS</u> WERE COOL!"

Y	A	C	R	B	L	U	S	E
S	R	B	U	E	Y	C	L	A
L	U	E	S	C	A	Y	B	R
A	E	Y	L	S	B	R	U	C
C	S	R	Y	A	U	L	E	B
U	B	L	E	R	C	S	A	Y
E	C	U	B	L	R	A	Y	S
R	Y	S	A	U	E	B	C	L
B	L	A	C	Y	S	E	R	U

The Odd Couple

These celebrities got hitched in the '00s, but which couple didn't get the happily ever after they were hoping for and split before the decade's end?

Britney & K-Fed

Tom & Katie

Angelina & Brad

Spot the Difference

How good were you at using Bunsen burners, pipettes, test tubes, and microscopes in school? Now see how good you are at spotting the 6 subtle differences in these tricky photos. Good luck!

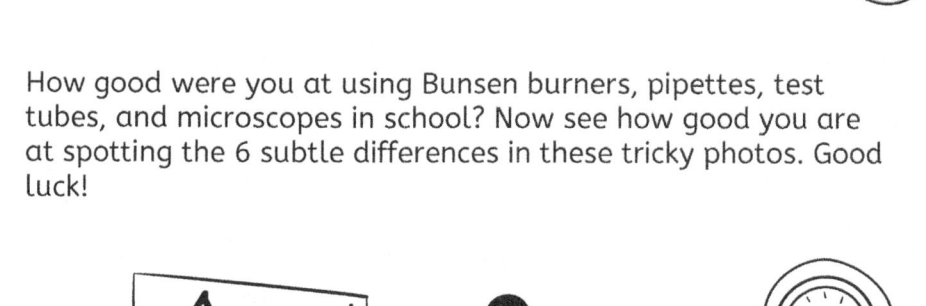

ARE ALWAYS THE HARDEST

Famous Whodunnit

They were legends and true gods of music in the '00s. But one of them took things too far backstage and ate all the brown M&Ms.

After arguing for hours and missing their performance, the police were called and interrogated the five suspects. Can you guess the guilty party if only three of the following statements are true?

1. Justin: 'JC did it.'
2. Lance: 'It wasn't me.'
3. Joey: 'Chris is innocent.'
4. JC: 'Justin is lying when he accuses me.'
5. Chris: 'Lance is telling the truth.'

Cheeky Chris ate them! Check the statements in the table below and notice that only Chris has three ticks against his name, meaning that the three statements given by Lance, JC and Chris were true.

Culprit	Statements				
	Justin	Lance	Joey	JC	Chris
Justin		√	√	√	√
Lance			√	√	
Joey		√	√	√	√
JC	√	√	√		√
Chris		√		√	√

Song Search

The titles of six best-selling songs from the '00s that had you busting a move at the school disco are hidden below. Can you find and circle them?

```
A  I  L  E  V  A  P  H  H  B  Q  V  V  H
V  D  U  R  L  Z  U  R  M  N  T  Y  O  A
Z  Q  U  E  X  J  X  V  L  A  F  W  N  V
F  P  Z  D  Q  H  J  M  V  C  Y  Z  X  K
J  R  E  G  G  I  D  D  L  O  G  A  L  G
L  S  L  S  B  V  F  I  U  X  T  N  N  O
E  R  Q  X  O  H  U  R  V  B  H  I  J  M
T  J  T  Y  Q  L  E  V  P  H  L  R  S  J
M  U  F  W  M  M  O  U  Z  E  U  Y  P  Y
E  I  H  Z  I  K  R  J  E  D  X  T  M  D
L  B  Y  N  J  L  S  F  N  D  M  U  N  J
O  Y  D  P  O  B  A  E  C  Q  J  Z  A  T
V  M  X  W  N  T  V  M  D  E  L  Z  A  I
E  O  Z  Q  T  Z  I  L  N  H  Y  I  Q  K
Y  K  B  O  K  Y  T  P  X  S  D  J  W  P
O  R  G  M  G  B  U  L  C  A  D  N  I  J
U  I  E  O  Y  E  V  D  B  F  T  O  S  B
```

ARE ALWAYS THE HARDEST

Pastime NPP

In any order you wish, copy the contents of each square in the jumbled picture below to the same numbered square in the blank grid on the next page until the entire puzzle is done, then add vivid '00s shades to your masterpiece.

Name the Movie 2

Guess the classic movies that '00s teens adored from these legendary quotes.

"It doesn't even have a first name – it just says McLovin!"

Superbad

"Go f**k yourself San Diego!"

Anchorman

"Please bore someone else with your questions."

Devil Wears Prada

"You're impossibly fast, and strong. Your skin is pale white and ice cold. Your eyes change color, and sometimes you speak like – like you're from a different time."

Twilight

"Even the smallest person can change the course of the future."

The Lord of the Rings

Past Price Is Right

The cost of stuff skyrocketed in recent times. But can you guess how much these young adult essentials cost in the '00s?

---------- Cinema Ticket ----------

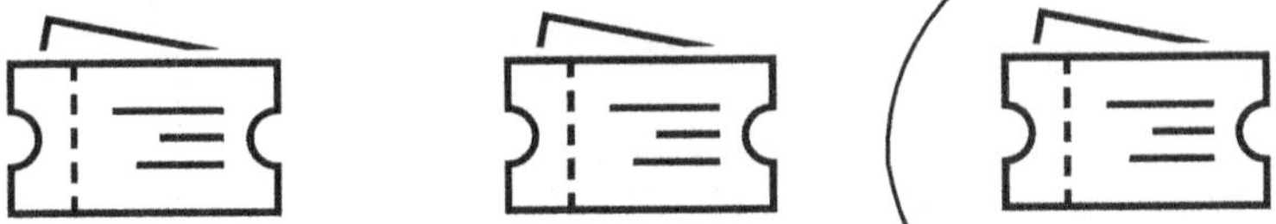

$4.39

$3.39

$5.39

---------- Packet of Cigarettes ----------

$3.89

$2.19

$4.69

---------- Six-pack of Beer ----------

$4.92

$6.32

$5.72

THE FIRST 30 YEARS OF CHILDHOOD

ARE ALWAYS THE HARDEST

THE FIRST 30 YEARS OF CHILDHOOD

BONUS: Badge

To make your milestone birthday even more special, here is an exclusive and exquisite badge for you to cut out and wear with PRIDE.

Go on... let everyone know just how grateful you were to be a '90s kid!

#90s kid

ARE ALWAYS THE HARDEST

THE FIRST 30 YEARS OF CHILDHOOD

More From Life in Puzzle

Did you enjoy your journey back through simpler times? I hope it brought back many happy memories and made you laugh.

If you want more giggle-inspiring books to lighten the mood, I've got you covered.

See all popular books and latest releases at

lifeinpuzzle.com

ARE ALWAYS THE HARDEST

THE FIRST 30 YEARS OF CHILDHOOD

HAPPY 30TH BIRTHDAY

YOU HAVE TO GET OLDER BUT YOU NEVER HAVE TO GROW UP!

ARE ALWAYS THE HARDEST

THE FIRST 30 YEARS OF CHILDHOOD

Wacky World News 1990-2009

1992: Wayne's World, shot on a modest budget in just 34 days, was released It's the only movie based on an SNL sketch to gross over $100,000,000 to date.

In 1992, Bryan Berg built a house of cards with 75 levels in Spirit Lake, Iowa, USA. Although it set a record for the tallest house of cards ever, he later broke his own record several times more.

In 1995, Ty decided to stop producing (aka "retire") Beanie Babies that were still selling. Selling only 36 of any one animal to independent retailers at a time created a market frenzy. There are numerous stories of the crazy lengths people went to get their hands on one including a woman who had her car broken into and retired Beanie Baby stolen from the dashboard. The thief left the radio untouched!

In 1996, Dolly the female Finnish Dorset sheep became the first ever mammal cloned from an adult somatic cell. Both the public and the scientific world were extremely excited about the achievement.

In 1997, Peter Beaumont set the fastest time across the Waen Rhydd bog at the 1997 World Bog Snorkelling Championships in Llanwrtyd Wells, Powys, Wales.

In 1997, the costs of filming Titanic eventually reached $200 million; a whopping $1 million per minute of screen time. Seemingly worth every penny, Titanic was the first movie ever to reach the billion-dollar mark and remained the highest-grossing film of all time until Avatar surpassed it in 2010.

In 2000, Microsoft released The Sims, the first game in the series, for Windows. It gave us whole new universes to build and explore.

In 2000, Guinness World Records acknowledged Ann Atkin West Putford, Devon, England as world record holder for the largest collection of gnomes and pixies. She recently sold the collection of over 2,000 garden gnomes with estimated worth over £100k.

In 2001, horror director Steve Miner spent $38,000,000 making Texas Rangers – a western movie about a small group of Texas Rangers trying to protect the West after the end of the American Civil War. It grossed less than a million dollars worldwide and is considered as one of the greatest movie flops of all time.

In 2001, the parents of children at Ley Hill School and Pre-School, Chesham, Buckinghamshire, UK made the world's longest Christmas cracker. It measured 207 ft long and 13 ft in diameter and contained balloons, toys, a hat (8ft in diameter) and a joke. Yes, the cracker went bang.

THE FIRST 30 YEARS OF CHILDHOOD

In 2005, Motorola released The Razr. Super thin. Customizable wallpaper. Front-facing camera for optimal selfies before selfies were even a thing. Basically, the coolest phone anyone could ever own.

In 2005, Sesame Street introduced the world to Veggie Monster. For some reason, "me want fruits and vegetables" wasn't as popular with kids as Cookie Monster's famous phrase.

But the wackiest event of all? ... You were born!

THE FIRST 30 YEARS OF CHILDHOOD